Crowned Image Publishing
Copyright © 2018

Printed in the United States of America.

ISBN-13: 978-1-946622-04-4

FOLLOWING JESUS

2019 LIFE REACH JOURNAL

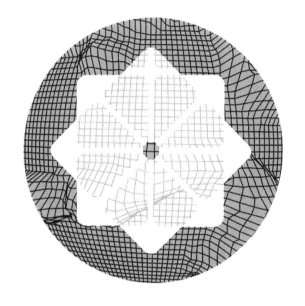

"THEN HE SAID TO THEM ALL,

'IF ANYONE DESIRES TO COME AFTER ME,
LET HIM DENY HIMSELF, AND TAKE UP
HIS CROSS DAILY, AND FOLLOW ME.'"

LUKE 9:23

_____

name

_____

date started

_____

date completed

USING YOUR
LIFE REACH JOURNAL

As a disciple of Jesus Christ, you must engage and encounter God the Father and Jesus the Son in the secret place, as you ask the Holy Spirit to lead you to love, look, listen, learn and live. Using the Life Reach Journal will help you to become anchored in and committed to these spiritual disciplines.

LOVE

(Mark 12:29-31; John 13:34-35)
Love the Father, Son and Holy Spirit with all your heart, mind, soul and strength. Love the Scriptures as your inspired guide through and in every area of life. Love the privileged position given to you, making you able to come before the throne of grace every day personally and intimately in prayer for yourself, your family, your friends and those in the world.

LOOK

(Isaiah 45:22; Hebrews 12:1-2)
Look to God in daily prayer and praise. Look into the word of God with an eye toward observation, interpretation, application, meditation and memorization. Look for revelation the Holy Spirit may show you to provide you with the knowledge, wisdom and spiritual understanding you need to move with clarity and confidence.

LISTEN

(John 16:13-15; Revelation 2:7; Ephesians 4:11-12)
Listen to the Holy Spirit as He leads you in your study of the Scriptures and in the ministry of prayer and praise. Listen to the *Walking Through the Word*[1] podcast as a resource for becoming more familiar with what the Scripture says, what it means and how to apply it in your life. Listen to and look at the *Starting in the Word*[2] videos, meant to give you bite-sized truths to encourage your heart and enable your journey with Jesus.

LEARN

(II Timothy 2:15; Joshua 1:8)
Learn by writing down your points of observation, interpretation and application from the Scriptures in your Life Reach Journal. Learn by meditating deeply on certain Scriptures and committing them to memory. Learn by looking and listening to those God has placed in your life, to better help you to understand God's word, will and ways.

LIVE

(Colossians 1:9-10; James 2:22-25)
Live out what you have received in the secret place by taking your Life Reach Journal with you wherever you go as a reference and reminder of what you heard and written down. Live out what you have received in the secret place, by looking for opportunities to share it with others in the gathering place and the public place. Live out what you have received in the secret place by letting every day be another step on the path of your journey with Jesus.

---

[1] The Walking Through The Word podcast is available on iTunes. Search "Walking Through The Word with Pastor Dale Evrist".

[2] The Starting In The Word videos are available on YouTube. Search "Starting In The Word".

REACHING NEIGHBORS NATIONS AND GENERATIONS WITH THE GOOD NEWS OF JESUS CHRIST'S LOVE AND POWER.

VISION STATEMENTS

⊕ Reach UP To God

Through the ministry of prayer and praise.

⊛ Reach IN To One Another

Through the ministry of making disciples, and the ministry of developing leaders and multiplying covenantal communities.

⬌ Reach OUT To The World

Through the ministry of evangelism, and the ministry of compassion and justice.

- ## The Ministry of Prayer and Praise
  ### (Matthew 6:6, Psalm 145:2)

  The Ministry of Prayer and Praise is about lifting up God's great name for who He is and what He's done and seeking God's face to discover His will and then agreeing with it in passion and faith.

- ## The Ministry of Evangelism and Making Disciples
  ### (Mark 16:15-16, Matthew 28:18-20)

  The Ministry of Evangelism and Making Disciples is about declaring and demonstrating the love and power of God's gospel (good news) in Jesus Christ and then teaching and training those who repent and believe the gospel to follow Jesus fully and faithfully.

- ## The Ministry of Developing Leaders and Multiplying Covenantal Communities (2 Timothy 2:2; Hebrews 10:24-25)

  The Ministry of Developing Leaders and Multiplying Covenantal Communities is about teaching and training Christ's disciples to love and lead those under their care, and increasing and strengthening committed Christian communities (families, Life Groups, healthy churches, etc.) that serve others with excellence.

- ## The Ministry of Compassion and Justice
  ### (Zechariah 7:9)

  The Ministry of Compassion and Justice is about righteously and resolutely serving the needs of the least and the lowest, the broken and the bound, the destitute and the downcast, and the oppressed and the outcast according to Christ's heart of love for them and as Christ's hands of life to them, spirit, soul and body.

REACH UP TO GOD
through the ministry
of prayer and praise.

As you engage daily in the ministry of prayer and praise, use the following scriptures to guide you. Use the spaces on the following pages to list both your requests to the Lord and when He answered.

PRAYER: But you, when you pray, go into your room, and when you have shut your door, pray to your Father who is in the secret place, and your Father who sees in secret will reward you openly (Matthew 6:6).

PRAISE: Every day I will bless You, And I will praise Your name forever and ever (Psalm 145:2).

PRAYING THE WAY JESUS TAUGHT

In this manner, therefore, pray: Our Father in heaven, hallowed be Your name. Your kingdom come. Your will be done on earth as it is in heaven. Give us this day our daily bread. And forgive us our debts, as we forgive our debtors. And do not lead us into temptation, but deliver us from the evil one. For Yours is the kingdom and the power and the glory forever. Amen (Matthew 6:9-13).

"OUR FATHER IN HEAVEN":

Affirm your identity as a child of God.

"HALLOWED BE YOUR NAME":

Hallowed means held in awe, revered. Praise and thank God for who He is, what He has done, and what He will do. As the Holy Spirit leads, include in your prayer the names of God:

THE NAMES OF GOD:

• **El Elyon** | "God Most High" (Gen.14:18)

• **El Roi** | "God Who Sees" (Gen.16:13)

• **El Shaddai** | "God Almighty" (Gen.17:1)

• **Yahweh Jireh** | "The Lord Will Provide" (Gen.22:14)

• **Yahweh Rophe** | "The Lord Who Heals" (Exo.15:26)

• **Yahweh Nissi** | "The Lord My Banner" (Exo.17:15)

• **Yahweh M'Kaddesh** | "The Lord Who Sanctifies You" (Exo.31:13)

• **Yahweh Shalom** | "The Lord Is Peace" (Jdg.6:24)

• **Yahweh Rohi** | "The Lord My Shepherd" (Psa.23:1)

• **Yahweh Tsidkenu** | "The Lord Our Righteousness" (Jer.23:6)

• **Yahweh Sabaoth** | "The Lord of Hosts" (1 Sam.1:3)

• **Yahweh Shammah** | "The Lord Is There" (Eze.48:35)

"YOUR KINGDOM COME. YOUR WILL BE DONE ON EARTH AS IT IS IN HEAVEN":

Pray for God's purposes and plans:
Globally | Nationally | Locally | Congregationally | Personally

"GIVE US THIS DAY OUR DAILY BREAD":

You never know how much God will get to you if He knows He can get it through you (to others). God promises to meet our needs, but we are to show our dependency on Him and ask for what we need to receive from Him for others. Pray dependently, consistently, specifically, and expectantly for your and others' physical, emotional and spiritual needs.

"FORGIVE US OUR DEBTS, AS WE FORGIVE OUR DEBTORS":

Ask the Holy Spirit to show you where you need to:
- Receive God's forgiveness for your sins through confession, repentance and cleansing (1 John 1:9).
- Release God's forgiveness to others who have sinned against you, and cancel their debt (Mark 11:25-26).

"DO NOT LEAD US (ALLOW US TO BE LED) INTO TEMPTATION, BUT DELIVER US FROM THE EVIL ONE":

Take particular areas of temptation before the Lord, surrendering to God's strength and protection. Take authority over the enemy, committing both to resist his attacks and not to go where you shouldn't be, as there is no grace to resist temptation in those circumstances.

"YOURS IS THE KINGDOM AND THE POWER AND THE GLORY FOREVER":

- The Kingdom: Rest in the knowledge that God's rule and dominion is working in and around us.
- The Power: Rely on God's dynamic, abundant, mighty, miracle-working, and creative power, knowing that we stand and fight from a place of victory.
- The Glory: Reflect God's excellence, honor, beauty, majesty and splendor to the world!

SCRIPTURES FOR COMMON PRAYER NEEDS

When we pray Scripture, we come into agreement with the truth of God's Word. Just as an anchor keeps a ship from being tossed to and fro, the Word of God is an anchor for our prayers that gives us a guide so that we are not moved off course. When we use His Word in prayer, we walk in the authority and power of His truth. In this section, many common prayer needs have been outlined to help you as you grow in the ministry of prayer.

(All Scripture quotations listed in this section are taken from the New King James Version®. Copyright © 1982 by Thomas Nelson. Used by permission. All rights reserved.)

RELATIONSHIP WITH GOD

+ And I will pray the Father, and He will give you another Helper, that He may abide with you forever— the Spirit of truth, whom the world cannot receive, because it neither sees Him nor knows Him; but you know Him, for He dwells with you and will be in you. (John 14:16-17)Jesus answered and said to him, "If anyone loves Me, he will keep My word; and My Father will love him, and We will come to him and make Our home with him." (John 14:23)Jesus said to him, "'You shall love the Lord your God with all your heart, with all your soul, and with all your mind." (Matthew 22:37)

+ For God so loved the world that He gave His only begotten Son, that whoever believes in Him should not perish but have everlasting life. (John 3:16)

+ For I am persuaded that neither death nor life, nor angels nor principalities nor powers, nor things present nor things to come, nor height nor depth, nor any other created thing, shall be able to separate us from the love of God which is in Christ Jesus our Lord. (Romans 8:38-39)

PEACE

+ Blessed are the peacemakers, for they shall be called sons of God. (Matthew 5:9)

+ Glory to God in the highest, and on earth peace, goodwill toward men! (Luke 2:14)

HEALING

+ But He was wounded for our transgressions, He was bruised for our iniquities; The chastisement for our peace was upon Him, and by His stripes we are healed. (Isaiah 53:5)

+ He Himself bore our sins in His own body on the tree, that we, having died to sins, might live for righteousness—by whose stripes you were healed. (1 Peter 2:24)

+ Behold, I give you the authority to trample on serpents and scorpions, and over all the power of the enemy, and nothing shall by any means hurt you. (Luke 10:19)

+ Assuredly, I say to you, whatever you bind on earth will be bound in heaven, and whatever you loose on earth will be loosed in heaven. Again I say to you that if two of you agree on earth concerning anything that they ask, it will be done for them by My Father in heaven. (Matthew 18:18-19)

+ If you diligently heed the voice of the Lord your God and do what is right in His sight, give ear to His commandments and keep all His statutes, I will put none of the diseases on you which I have brought on the Egyptians. For I am the Lord who heals you. (Exodus 15:26)

+ And my God shall supply all your need according to His riches in glory by Christ Jesus. (Philippians 4:19)

UNBELIEVERS

+ Then God said, "Let there be light"; and there was light. (Genesis 1:3)

+ For it is the God who commanded light to shine out of darkness, who has shone in our hearts to give the light of the knowledge of the glory of God in the face of Jesus Christ. (2 Corinthians 4:6)

+ Let your light so shine before men, that they may see your good works and glorify your Father in heaven. (Matthew 5:16)

+ And when He has come, He will convict the world of sin, and of righteousness, and of judgment: (John 16:8)

+ For God so loved the world that He gave His only begotten Son, that whoever believes in Him should not perish but have everlasting life. (John 3:16)

+ … having your conduct honorable among the Gentiles, that when they speak against you as evildoers, they may, by your good works which they observe, glorify God in the day of visitation. (1 Peter 2:12)

FEAR

+ When you lie down, you will not be afraid; Yes, you will lie down and your sleep will be sweet. (Proverbs 3:24)

+ Keep me as the apple of Your eye; Hide me under the shadow of Your wings. (Psalm 17:8)

+ For God has not given us a spirit of fear, but of power and of love and of a sound mind. (2 Timothy 1:7)

+ Because you have made the Lord, *who is* my refuge, Even the Most High, your dwelling place, No evil shall befall you, Nor shall any plague come near your dwelling; (Psalm 91:9-10)

FRIENDSHIPS

+ ...having your conduct honorable among the Gentiles, that when they speak against you as evildoers, they may, by *your* good works which they observe, glorify God in the day of visitation. (1 Peter 2:12)

+ A friend loves at all times, and a brother is born for adversity. (Proverbs 17:17)

+ By this all will know that you are My disciples, if you have love for one another. (John 13:35)

+ Can two walk together, unless they are agreed? (Amos 3:3)

+ These things I command you, that you love one another. (John 15:17)

+ Behold, how good and how pleasant it is for brethren to dwell together in unity! (Psalm 133:1)

FAMILY

+ God sets the solitary in families; He brings out those who are bound into prosperity; But the rebellious dwell in a dry land. (Psalm 68:6)

+ And he will turn the hearts of the fathers to the children, and the hearts of the children to their fathers, lest I come and strike the earth with a curse. (Malachi 4:6)

+ Children, obey your parents in the Lord, for this is right. "Honor your father and mother," which is the first commandment with promise: "that it may be well with you and you may live long on the earth." (Ephesians 6:1-3)

+ And you, fathers, do not provoke your children to wrath, but bring them up in the training and admonition of the Lord. (Ephesians 6:4)

+ Children, obey your parents in all things, for this is well pleasing to the Lord. Fathers, do not provoke your children, lest they become discouraged. (Colossians 3:20-21)

SAFETY

+ I will both lie down in peace, and sleep; For You alone, O Lord, make me dwell in safety. (Psalm 4:8)

+ "For I will surely deliver you, and you shall not fall by the sword; but your life shall be as a prize to you, because you have put your trust in Me," says the Lord. (Jeremiah 39:18)

+ The Lord also will be a refuge for the oppressed, a refuge in times of trouble. (Psalm 9:9)

+ And have not shut me up into the hand of the enemy; You have set my feet in a wide place. (Psalm 31:8)

+ The name of the Lord is a strong tower; The righteous run to it and are safe. (Proverbs 18:10)

+ I do not pray that You should take them out of the world, but that You should keep them from the evil one. (John 17:5)

OBEDIENCE

+ I will never forget Your precepts, for by them You have given me life. (Psalm 119:93)

+ Children, obey your parents in the Lord, for this is right. (Ephesians 6:1)

+ He who is not with Me is against Me, and he who does not gather with Me scatters. (Luke 11:23)

LOVING OTHERS

+ Lord, who may abide in Your tabernacle? Who may dwell in Your holy hill? He who walks uprightly, and works righteousness, and speaks the truth in his heart; He who does not backbite with his tongue, nor does evil to his neighbor, nor does he take up a reproach against his friend; In whose eyes a vile person is despised, but he honors those who fear the Lord; He who swears to his own hurt and does not change; (Psalm 15:1-4)

+ Beloved, let us love one another, for love is of God; and everyone who loves is born of God and knows God. (1 John 4:7)

+ My little children, let us not love in word or in tongue, but in deed and in truth. (1 John 3:18)

+ But I say to you, love your enemies, bless those who curse you, do good to those who hate you, and pray for those who spitefully use you and persecute you, that you may be sons of your Father in heaven; for He makes His sun rise on the evil and on the good, and sends rain on the just and on the unjust. (Matthew 5:44-45)

+ Finally, all of you be of one mind, having compassion for one another; love as brothers, be tenderhearted, be courteous; (1 Peter 3:8)

+ By this all will know that you are My disciples, if you have love for one another. (John 13:35)

UNITY WITH FAMILY AND FRIENDS

+ If you were pure and upright, surely now He would awake for you, and prosper your rightful dwelling place. (Job 8:6)

+ Live worthy of the calling you have received, with all lowliness and gentleness, with longsuffering, bearing with one another in love, endeavoring to keep the unity of the Spirit in the bond of peace. (Ephesians 4:1-3)

+ Now the multitude of those who believed were of one heart and one soul; neither did anyone say that any of the things he possessed was his own, but they had all things in common.
(Acts 4:32)

+ Fulfill my joy by being like-minded, having the same love, being of one accord, of one mind. (Philippians 2:2)

DAILY WALKING THROUGH THE WORD

All Scripture is given by inspiration of God, and is profitable for doctrine, for reproof, for correction, for instruction in righteousness, that the man of God may be complete, thoroughly equipped for every good work (2 Timothy 3:16-17).

Inductive Bible Study: As you study the Word, use these Inductive Bible Study guidelines to help you better understand what each passage of scripture is saying, what it means, and how to apply it.

OBSERVATION: Observation teaches you to see exactly what the passage says. It is the basis for accurate interpretation and correct application. Observation answers the question, "What does the passage say?"

INTERPRETATION: While observation leads to an accurate understanding of what the Word of God says, interpretation goes a step further and helps you understand what it means in the context in which it was written.

APPLICATION: The first step in application is to find out what the Word of God says on any particular subject through accurate and correct interpretation of the text. Once you understand what the Word of God teaches, you then obey the truths by applying them to your life.

WALKING THROUGH THE WORD PODCAST

Walk through the word with New Song Nashville's devotional commentary from the depths of the Scriptures. If you have been challenged in knowing how to apply the truths that are buried in the Word to your life, listen for an overview of the daily Old Testament and New Testament readings and a central theme with some helpful points of application.

To access, search in your mobile app for "Walking Through The Word Podcast" or go to newsongnashville.com and click on the podcast icon at the bottom of the page.

THE THEOLOGY OF PLACE

The Bible teaches that there are three main places that we are to engage in ministry unto the Lord and unto others: The Secret Place, The Gathering Place and The Public Place. It is important that we develop a sound Theology of Place, recognizing where we are to go and what we are to do to live our lives for the glory of God and the good of others, place-by-place, purpose-by-purpose and person-by-person.

THE SECRET PLACE (Matthew 6:6)
In the Secret Place we are to meet alone with God the Father and Jesus the Son by the life and leading of the Holy Spirit. The Secret Place is a place where a private, personal and intimate relationship with God can be cultivated in the word and in prayer and praise. It is in The Secret Place where a private spiritual history is established which then becomes a public spiritual history in The Gathering Place and The Public Place.

THE GATHERING PLACE (Matthew 18:18-20)
In the Gathering Place we are to come together with the people of God, gathered in the name of Jesus, looking to minister to one another according to the truth of the word and the person and power of the Holy Spirit. These gatherings can be as small as two or as many as thousands who agree together for the presence of Jesus to reveal and release His light and life. From the Gathering Place we move to the Public Place.

THE PUBLIC PLACE (Acts 2:46-47)
In the Public Place we release to a lost and broken world a relevant witness from a revived people—a people full of the word and the Spirit, received in the Secret Place and the Gathering Place. It is in this place where The Theology of Place finds its point of missional completion as neighbors, nations and generations are reached with the good news of Jesus Christ's love and power, person-by-person, need-by-need.

REACH IN TO ONE ANOTHER

through the ministry of making disciples, and the ministry of developing leaders and multiplying covenantal communities.

MAKING DISCIPLES: And Jesus came and spoke to them, saying, "All authority has been given to Me in heaven and on earth. Go therefore and make disciples of all the nations, baptizing them in the name of the Father and of the Son and of the Holy Spirit, teaching them to observe all things that I have commanded you; and lo, I am with you always, even to the end of the age." Amen (Matthew 28:18-20).

DEVELOPING LEADERS: And the things that you have heard from me among many witnesses, commit these to faithful men who will be able to teach others also (2 Timothy 2:2).

MULTIPLYING COVENANTAL COMMUNITIES: And let us consider one another in order to stir up love and good works, not forsaking the assembling of ourselves together, as is the manner of some, but exhorting one another, and so much the more as you see the day approaching (Hebrews 10:24-25).

LIFE REACH SCHOOL OF MINISTRY provides a context for our New Song family to lovingly serve and equip one another to reach our full potential in Christ at every age and every stage. We accomplish this by discipling to Christ, mentoring to task, and coaching to excellence.

LIFE REACH SCHOOL OF MINISTRY INCLUDES:

- Age-Based Discipling
- Life Groups
- Equipping Groups
- Leadership Training
- Topic-focused Seminars
- Resources and Publications

REACH OUT TO THE WORLD

through the ministry of evangelism,
and the ministry of compassion and justice.

EVANGELISM: And [Jesus] said to them, "Go into all the world and preach the gospel to every creature. He who believes and is baptized will be saved; but he who does not believe will be condemned" (Mark 16:15-16).

COMPASSION AND JUSTICE: Thus says the Lord of hosts: "Execute true justice, show mercy and compassion everyone to his brother" (Zechariah 7:9).

THE GOSPEL CREED

The GOSPEL is the GOOD NEWS that God became man in Jesus Christ. He lived the life we should have lived and died the death we should have died—in our place. Three days later He rose from the dead, proving that He is the Son of God and offering the gift of salvation and forgiveness of sins to everyone who repents and believes in Him.*

* ricebroocks.com/blog/what-is-the-gospel/

MissionTEN.9

Over the 2010-2019 decade, our New Song family is committed to seeing ten years of the greatest ministry we have ever known. We believe during this "Decade of the King" we will see a ten-year stretch of time where King Jesus is glorified in the earth in an unparalleled way in our experience as we serve Jesus by serving the needs of people in our community, in our state, our nation and in our world. MissionTEN.9 is the final year of this "Decade of the King," where New Song is committed to the following areas:

+   **Personal Evangelism:** Job #1 for us is to get out into the harvest field of our community and lead lost people to Christ. God has called us to reach those within our reach by the declaration and demonstration of the Gospel of the Kingdom wherever we go and in whatever places God sends us. Paul teaches us in Romans 1:16-17 not to be ashamed of the gospel because "it is the power of God to salvation for everyone who believes." We believe God is calling all of us to share the gospel personally and powerfully with every person in our spheres of influence.

+   **Multiplication of Covenantal Communities:** Multiplying covenantal communities is one of our New Song ministry values and is the heart of what we are doing to reach our city for Christ. Rather than just being a "come-to" church, it is our goal to be a "go-to" church to more effectively and personally reach people where they are through the multiplication of covenantal communities such as Life Groups, Equipping Groups, discipleship groups, and more throughout the Greater Nashville area. By doing this, the people of New Song are in their communities close to the needs and are ready, willing and able to meet those needs. We believe this is our most effective way to get out and into the lives of the most people possible.

+ **Community Partners:** We believe it is vital to seek both to know the needs of our community and to meet those needs, and in the process, to share the life and light of Jesus Christ. Community Partners are ministries of compassion and justice with whom we serve the needs in our community while sharing the good news of Jesus Christ's love and power. We have made a commitment to serve and bless our community by establishing and strengthening covenantal relationships with local ministry partners.

+ **Global Partners:** God has given us global assignments with specific peoples and nations where we are to advance His Kingdom with His good news, love and power. In 2019 we will continue to focus on our Strategic Global Assignments—India, Italy, Mexico, Kenya and Nepal— in addition to other projects locally and globally. To do this, we walk in covenantal relationship with missionaries serving in the nations, and we are committed to helping them have the resources they need to accomplish the tasks that God has given them.

+ **GOTeams:** We are called to make an indelible mark for the gospel as we partner with missionaries around the world by going and helping them strengthen ministry that is permanent and ongoing. We will send short-term Gospel Outreach Teams (GOTeams) in response to the needs of our Global Partners, providing an opportunity for members of New Song to serve in the nations around the globe. In so doing, we commit to learn, love and serve everywhere our teams go to impact the nations for His Kingdom.

HELP US REACH OUR FINANCIAL GOAL FOR MISSIONTEN.9! HERE'S HOW:

- Mail your contributions to: New Song MissionTEN.9 316 Southgate Court // Brentwood TN 37027
- Give online: NewSongNashville.com
- Put your contribution in the MissionTEN.9 basket at church on Sunday

PERSONAL VISION & GOALS

Take some time to pray and ask the Lord to reveal through His Holy Spirit what His vision and goals are for you in this coming season, and write them down. Share them with a few trusted friends and leaders, and pray into them regularly.

SPIRITUAL | I will instruct you and teach you in the way you should go; I will guide you with My eye (Psalm 32:8).

_____
_____
_____
_____
_____
_____
_____

PERSONAL | For we are His workmanship, created in Christ Jesus for good works, which God prepared beforehand that we should walk in them. (Ephesians 2:10).

_____
_____
_____
_____
_____
_____
_____
_____
_____

EDUCATIONAL | Happy is the man who finds wisdom, and the man who gains understanding (Proverbs 3:13).

_____
_____
_____
_____
_____
_____
_____
_____
_____
_____

RELATIONAL | By this all will know that you are My disciples, if you have love for one another (John 13:35).

_____
_____
_____
_____
_____
_____
_____
_____
_____
_____
_____
_____
_____

Personal
Vision
& Goals

HEALTH & FITNESS | Or do you not know that your body is the temple of the Holy Spirit who is in you, whom you have from God, and you are not your own? For you were bought at a price; therefore glorify God in your body and in your spirit, which are God's (1 Corinthians 6:19-20).

_____

_____

_____

_____

_____

_____

_____

_____

_____

_____

FINANCIAL | The generous soul will be made rich, and he who waters will also be watered himself (Proverbs 11:25).

_____

_____

_____

_____

_____

_____

_____

_____

_____

_____

_____

Personal
Vision
& Goals

HOME & FAMILY | And if it seems evil to you to serve the Lord, choose for yourselves this day whom you will serve, whether the gods which your fathers served that were on the other side of the River, or the gods of the Amorites, in whose land you dwell. But as for me and my house, we will serve the Lord (Joshua 24:15).

Ministry | And He said to them, "Go into all the world and preach the gospel to every creature..." (Mark 16:15).

JANUARY 2019

	Old Testament	New Testament	Psalms	Proverbs
1	Gen 1:1-2:25	Matt 1:1-2:12	1:1-6	1:1-6
2	Gen 3:1-4:26	Matt 2:13-3:6	2:1-12	1:7-9
3	Gen 5:1-7:24	Matt 3:7-4:11	3:1-8	1:10-19
4	Gen 8:1-10:32	Matt 4:12-25	4:1-8	1:20-23
5	Gen 11:1-12:20	Matt 5:1-26	5:1-12	1:24-28
6	Gen 13:1-15:21	Matt 5:27-48	6:1-10	1:29-33
7	Gen 16:1-18:15	Matt 6:1-24	7:1-17	2:1-5
8	Gen 18:16-19:38	Matt 6:25-7:14	8:1-9	2:6-15
9	Gen 20:1-22:24	Matt 7:15-29	9:1-10	2:16-22
10	Gen 23:1-24:67	Matt 8:1-17	9:11-20	3:1-6
11	Gen 25:1-26:17	Matt 8:18-34	10:1-7	3:7-8
12	Gen 26:18-27:46	Matt 9:1-17	10:8-18	3:9-10
13	Gen 28:1-29:35	Matt 9:18-38	11:1-7	3:11-12
14	Gen 30:1-31:21	Matt 10:1-26	12:1-8	3:13-15
15	Gen 31:22-32:12	Matt 10:27-11:6	13:1-6	3:16-18
16	Gen 32:13-34:31	Matt 11:7-30	14:1-7	3:19-20
17	Gen 35:1-36:43	Matt 12:1-21	15:1-5	3:21-26
18	Gen 37:1-38:30	Matt 12:22-45	16:1-11	3:27-32
19	Gen 39:1-41:16	Matt 12:46-13:23	17:1-15	3:33-35
20	Gen 41:17-42:17	Matt 13:24-46	18:1-15	4:1-6
21	Gen 42:18-43:34	Matt 13:47-14:12	18:16-34	4:7-9
22	Gen 44:1-45:28	Matt 14:13-36	18:35-50	4:10-13
23	Gen 46:1-47:31	Matt 15:1-28	19:1-14	4:14-19
24	Gen 48:1-49:33	Matt 15:29-16:12	20:1-9	4:20-27
25	Gen 50:1-Ex 2:10	Matt 16:13-17:9	21:1-13	5:1-6
26	Ex 2:11-3:22	Matt 17:10-27	22:1-15	5:7-14
27	Ex 4:1-5:21	Matt 18:1-20	22:16-31	5:15-21
28	Ex 5:22-7:25	Matt 18:21-19:12	23:1-6	5:22-23
29	Ex 8:1-9:35	Matt 19:13-30	24:1-10	6:1-5
30	Ex 10:1-12:13	Matt 20:1-28	25:1-11	6:6-11
31	Ex 12:14-13:16	Matt 20:29-21:22	25:12-22	6:12-15

KEY PASSAGES

_____
_____
_____
_____
_____
_____
_____
_____
_____
_____
_____
_____
_____

PRAYER REQUESTS

Date: **Request:**   **Date Answered:**

_____
_____
_____
_____
_____
_____
_____
_____
_____
_____
_____
_____
_____
_____
_____
_____
_____
_____

JANUARY 2019

Sunday	Monday	Tuesday	Wednesday
		1 New Year's Day	2
6 My four - boys - Suzy? cant commit?	7 It's me! paddy Issues childs song	8	9
13	14	15	16
20	21 Martin Luther King, Jr. Day	22	23
27	28	29	30

Thursday	Friday	Saturday
3	4 will you scribe?	5 be my
10	11 greatest year of following Jesus Holiness outside is	12
17 what is inside manifested appreciation not spoken feels like	18	19
24 under appreciation no appreciation at all family	25 appreciation at - Portico, friends,	26
31		

following Jesus

Notes

I don't
want to be
that person
any more

- Gavin

Dig your
well w/ Jesus
deeper

FEBRUARY 2019

	Old Testament	New Testament	Psalms	Proverbs
1	Ex 13:17-15:19	Matt 21:23-46	26:1-12	6:16-19
2	Ex 15:20-17:7	Matt 22:1-33	27:1-6	6:20-26
3	Ex 17:8-19:15	Matt 22:34-23:12	27:7-14	6:27-35
4	Ex 19:16-21:27	Matt 23:13-39	28:1-9	7:1-5
5	Ex 21:28-23:13	Matt 24:1-28	29:1-11	7:6-23
6	Ex 23:14-25:40	Matt 24:29-51	30:1-12	7:24-27
7	Ex 26:1-27:21	Matt 25:1-30	31:1-8	8:1-11
8	Ex 28:1-43	Matt 25:31-26:13	31:9-18	8:12-13
9	Ex 29:1-30:10	Matt 26:14-46	31:19-24	8:14-26
10	Ex 30:11-31:18	Matt 26:47-68	32:1-11	8:27-31
11	Ex 32:1-33:23	Matt 26:69-27:14	33:1-12	8:32-36
12	Ex 34:1-35:9	Matt 27:15-37	33:13-22	9:1-6
13	Ex 35:10-36:38	Matt 27:38-66	34:1-10	9:7-8
14	Ex 37:1-38:31	Matt 28:1-20	34:11-22	9:9-10
15	Ex 39:1-40:38	Mark 1:1-28	35:1-16	9:11-12
16	Lev 1:1-3:17	Mark 1:29-2:12	35:17-28	9:13-18
17	Lev 4:1-5:19	Mark 2:13-3:6	36:1-12	10:1-2
18	Lev 6:1-7:27	Mark 3:7-30	37:1-11	10:3-4
19	Lev 7:28-9:6	Mark 3:31-4:25	37:12-28	10:5
20	Lev 9:7-10:20	Mark 4:26-5:20	37:29-40	10:6-7
21	Lev 11:1-12:8	Mark 5:21-43	38:1-22	10:8-9
22	Lev 13:1-59	Mark 6:1-29	39:1-13	10:10
23	Lev 14:1-57	Mark 6:30-56	40:1-10	10:11-12
24	Lev 15:1-16:34	Mark 7:1-23	40:11-17	10:13-14
25	Lev 17:1-18:30	Mark 7:24-8:10	41:1-13	10:15
26	Lev 19:1-20:21	Mark 8:11-38	42:1-11	10:16
27	Lev 20:22-22:16	Mark 9:1-29	43:1-5	10:17
28	Lev 22:17-23:44	Mark 9:30-10:12	44:1-12	10:18-19

KEY PASSAGES

Nashville	Assoc. Pastor
	NACRR
	- illness
Athens	- Apartment
	Bethany
	Joe
Pleasant Hill	- 2+ years
Albany Baptist	

PRAYER REQUESTS

Ⓑ

Date: Request: Date Answered:

Nashville	K + D - mercy
	- 15 years
New song	- 12 years

Family	Gone	where
	Dad	mike steve
	mom	Sharon
	Gary	Ron
	6. Barb	
	Aunts	- Phoenix
	Uncles	- nieces
		- nephews

FEBRUARY 2019

	Sunday	Monday	Tuesday	Wednesday
①	140 89 74			
② / ③	**3** 151 86 71 143	**4**	**5**	**6**
④	**10** 91 67 149 93 73	**11**	**12**	**13**
⑤ / ⑥	**17** 155 96 75 155	**18** President's Day	**19**	**20**
⑦	**24** 82 70 151 89	**25**	**26**	**27**

69

Dr. Phillips   8:45 AM fast

Thursday	Friday	Saturday
	1 *fatigue*	2
7	8 *anemia Thyroid sugar*	9
14 Valentine's Day	15	16
21	22	23
28		

Notes

foundation
John 14:21-24
- loving
and
obeying
- How strong
is my
salvation
- hear I do
- I will love
and reveal
myself to
the world
(HEALTH)

MARCH 2019

	Old Testament	New Testament	Psalms	Proverbs
1	Lev 24:1-25:46	Mark 10:13-31	44:13-26	10:20-21
2	Lev 25:47-27:13	Mark 10:32-52	45:1-17	10:22
3	Lev 27:14-Num 1:54	Mark 11:1-26	46:1-11	10:23
4	Num 2:1-3:51	Mark 11:27-12:17	47:1-9	10:24-25
5	Num 4:1-5:31	Mark 12:18-37	48:1-14	10:26
6	Num 6:1-7:89	Mark 12:38-13:13	49:1-20	10:27-28
7	Num 8:1-9:23	Mark 13:14-37	50:1-23	10:29-30
8	Num 10:1-11:23	Mark 14:1-21	51:1-19	10:31-32
9	Num 11:24-13:33	Mark 14:22-52	52:1-9	11:1-3
10	Num 14:1-15:21	Mark 14:53-72	53:1-6	11:4
11	Num 15:22-16:40	Mark 15:1-47	54:1-7	11:5-6
12	Num 16:41-18:32	Mark 16:1-20	55:1-23	11:7
13	Num 19:1-20:29	Luke 1:1-25	56:1-13	11:8
14	Num 21:1-22:21	Luke 1:26-56	57:1-11	11:9-11
15	Num 22:22-23:30	Luke 1:57-80	58:1-11	11:12-13
16	Num 24:1-25:18	Luke 2:1-35	59:1-17	11:14
17	Num 26:1-51	Luke 2:36-52	60:1-12	11:15
18	Num 26:52-28:15	Luke 3:1-22	61:1-8	11:16-17
19	Num 28:16-29:40	Luke 3:23-38	62:1-12	11:18-19
20	Num 30:1-31:54	Luke 4:1-30	63:1-11	11:20-21
21	Num 32:1-33:39	Luke 4:31-5:11	64:1-10	11:22
22	Num 33:40-35:34	Luke 5:12-26	65:1-13	11:23
23	Num 36:1-Deut 1:46	Luke 5:27-6:11	66:1-20	11:24-26
24	Deut 2:1-3:29	Luke 6:12-36	67:1-7	11:27
25	Deut 4:1-49	Luke 6:37-7:10	68:1-18	11:28
26	Deut 5:1-6:25	Luke 7:11-35	68:19-35	11:29-31
27	Deut 7:1-8:20	Luke 7:36-8:3	69:1-18	12:1
28	Deut 9:1-10:22	Luke 8:4-21	69:19-36	12:2-3
29	Deut 11:1-12:32	Luke 8:22-39	70:1-5	12:4
30	Deut 13:1-15:23	Luke 8:40-9:6	71:1-24	12:5-7
31	Deut 16:1-17:20	Luke 9:7-27	72:1-20	12:8-9

KEY PASSAGES

John 14: 21-24

PRAYER REQUESTS

Date: **Request:**   **Date Answered:**

MARCH 2019

Sunday	Monday	Tuesday	Wednesday
3	4	5	6
10 Daylight Saving (Start)	11	12	13
17 St. Patrick's Day	18	19	20
24 31	25	26	27

Thursday	Friday	Saturday
	1	2
7	8	9
14	15	16
21	22	23
28	29	30

Notes

_____
_____
_____
_____
_____
_____
_____
_____
_____
_____
_____
_____
_____
_____
_____
_____
_____
_____
_____
_____
_____
_____
_____
_____
_____
_____
_____
_____
_____
_____

APRIL 2019

	Old Testament	New Testament	Psalms	Proverbs
1	Deut 18:1-20:20	Luke 9:28-50	73:1-28	12:10
2	Deut 21:1-22:30	Luke 9:51-10:12	74:1-23	12:11
3	Deut 23:1-25:19	Luke 10:13-37	75:1-10	12:12-14
4	Deut 26:1-27:26	Luke 10:38-11:13	76:1-12	12:15-17
5	Deut 28:1-68	Luke 11:14-36	77:1-20	12:18
6	Deut 29:1-30:20	Luke 11:37-12:7	78:1-25	12:19-20
7	Deut 31:1-32:9	Luke 12:8-34	78:26-45	12:21-23
8	Deut 32:10-52	Luke 12:35-59	78:46-55	12:24
9	Deut 33:1-29	Luke 13:1-21	78:56-72	12:25
10	Deut 34:1-Josh 2:24	Luke 13:22-14:6	79:1-13	12:26
11	Josh 3:1-4:24	Luke 14:7-35	80:1-19	12:27-28
12	Josh 5:1-7:15	Luke 15:1-32	81:1-16	13:1
13	Josh 7:16-8:35	Luke 16:1-18	82:1-8	13:2-3
14	Josh 9:1-10:43	Luke 16:19-17:10	83:1-18	13:4
15	Josh 11:1-12:24	Luke 17:11-37	84:1-12	13:5-6
16	Josh 13:1-14:15	Luke 18:1-17	85:1-13	13:7-8
17	Josh 15:1-63	Luke 18:18-43	86:1-17	13:9-10
18	Josh 16:1-18:28	Luke 19:1-27	87:1-7	13:11
19	Josh 19:1-20:9	Luke 19:28-48	88:1-18	13:12-14
20	Josh 21:1-22:20	Luke 20:1-26	89:1-18	13:15-16
21	Josh 22:21-23:16	Luke 20:27-47	89:19-37	13:17-19
22	Josh 24:1-33	Luke 21:1-28	89:38-52	13:20-23
23	Judges 1:1-2:10	Luke 21:29-22:13	90:1-91:16	13:24-25
24	Judges 2:11-3:31	Luke 22:14-34	92:1-93:5	14:1-2
25	Judges 4:1-5:31	Luke 22:35-53	94:1-23	14:3-4
26	Judges 6:1-40	Luke 22:54-23:12	95:1-96:13	14:5-6
27	Judges 7:1-8:16	Luke 23:13-43	97:1-98:9	14:7-8
28	Judges 8:17-9:21	Luke 23:44-24:12	99:1-9	14:9-10
29	Judges 9:22- 10:18	Luke 24:13-53	100:1-5	14:11-12
30	Judges 11:1-12:15	John 1:1-28	101:1-8	14:13-14

KEY PASSAGES

soul - invisible part
of us which contains
our intellect

emotion + will
Guard your heart
... it determines everything

Romans 12: 1 + 2

do not be conformed

PRAYER REQUESTS

transformed - to be changed

- inside out
(seed) change

① Renew - meditate, memorize

- import "right thinking

? Prov 23:7 as he thinks

power, love, sound mind

Phil 2:7 whatever is good

- deeply, carefully

APRIL 2019

Sunday	Monday	Tuesday	Wednesday
	1	2	3
7	8	9	10
14	15	16	17
21 Easter	22	23	24
28	29	30	

Thursday	Friday	Saturday
4	5	6
11	12	13
18	19 Good Friday	20
25	26	27

I can't

I can do all things

Gods Grace

Gal 6:9

do not lose heart

MAY 2019

	Old Testament	New Testament	Psalms	Proverbs
1	Judges 13:1-14:20	John 1:29-51	102:1-28	14:15-16
2	Judges 15:1-16:31	John 2:1-25	103:1-22	14:17-19
3	Judges 17:1-18:31	John 3:1-21	104:1-18	14:20-21
4	Judges 19:1-20:48	John 3:22-4:4	104:19-35	14:22-24
5	Judges 21:1-Ruth 1:22	John 4:5-42	105:1-15	14:25
6	Ruth 2:1-4:22	John 4:43-54	105:16-36	14:26-27
7	I Sam 1:1-2:21	John 5:1-23	105:37-45	14:28-29
8	I Sam 2:22-4:22	John 5:24-47	106:1-23	14:30-31
9	I Sam 5:1-7:17	John 6:1-21	106:24-48	14:32-33
10	I Sam 8:1-9:26	John 6:22-40	107:1-16	14:34-35
11	I Sam 9:27-11:15	John 6:41-71	107:17-43	15:1-3
12	I Sam 12:1-13:23	John 7:1-24	108:1-13	15:4
13	I Sam 14:1-52	John 7:25-8:1	109:1-31	15:5-7
14	I Sam 15:1-16:23	John 8:2-20	110:1-7	15:8-10
15	I Sam 17:1-18:4	John 8:21-36	111:1-10	15:11
16	I Sam 18:5-19:24	John 8:37-59	112:1-10	15:12-14
17	I Sam 20:1-21:15	John 9:1-41	113:1-114:8	15:15-17
18	I Sam 22:1-23:29	John 10:1-21	115:1-18	15:18-19
19	I Sam 24:1-25:44	John 10:22-42	116:1-19	15:20-21
20	I Sam 26:1-28:25	John 11:1-54	117:1-2	15:22-23
21	I Sam 29:1-31:13	John 11:55-12:19	118:1-18	15:24-26
22	II Sam 1:1-2:11	John 12:20-50	118:19-29	15:27-28
23	II Sam 2:12-3:39	John 13:1-30	119:1-16	15:29-30
24	II Sam 4:1-6:23	John 13:31-14:18	119:17-32	15:31-32
25	II Sam 7:1-8:18	John 14:19-31	119:33-48	15:33
26	II Sam 9:1-11:27	John 15:1-27	119:49-64	16:1-3
27	II Sam 12:1-31	John 16:1-33	119:65-80	16:4-5
28	II Sam 13:1-39	John 17:1-26	119:81-96	16:6-7
29	II Sam 14:1-15:18	John 18:1-24	119:97-112	16:8-9
30	II Sam 15:19-16:23	John 18:25-19:24	119:113-128	16:10-11
31	II Sam 17:1-29	John 19:25-42	119:129-152	16:12-13

KEY PASSAGES

_____
_____
_____
_____
_____
_____
_____
_____
_____
_____
_____
_____
_____

PRAYER REQUESTS

Date: **Request:**   **Date Answered:**

_____
_____
_____
_____
_____
_____
_____
_____
_____
_____
_____
_____
_____
_____
_____
_____
_____
_____

MAY 2019

Sunday	Monday	Tuesday	Wednesday
			1
5 Cinco de Mayo	6	7	8
12 Mother's Day	13	14	15
19 Pentecost	20	21	22
26	27 Memorial Day	28	29

Thursday	Friday	Saturday
2 National Day of Prayer	3	4
9	10	11
16	17	18
23	24	25
30	31	

Notes

_____
_____
_____
_____
_____
_____
_____
_____
_____
_____
_____
_____
_____
_____
_____
_____
_____
_____
_____
_____
_____
_____
_____
_____
_____
_____
_____
_____
_____
_____
_____
_____
_____

JUNE 2019

	Old Testament	New Testament	Psalms	Proverbs
1	II Sam 18:1-19:8	John 20:1-31	119:153-176	16:14-15
2	II Sam 19:9-20:14	John 21:1-25	120:1-7	16:16-17
3	II Sam 20:15-22:20	Acts 1:1-26	121:1-8	16:18
4	II Sam 22:21-23:23	Acts 2:1-47	122:1-9	16:19-20
5	II Sam 23:24-24:25	Acts 3:1-26	123:1-4	16:21-23
6	I Kings 1:1-53	Acts 4:1-37	124:1-8	16:24
7	I Kings 2:1-46	Acts 5:1-42	125:1-5	16:25
8	I Kings 3:1-4:34	Acts 6:1-15	126:1-6	16:26-27
9	I Kings 5:1-6:38	Acts 7:1-29	127:1-5	16:28-30
10	I Kings 7:1-51	Acts 7:30-50	128:1-6	16:31-33
11	I Kings 8:1-66	Acts 7:51-8:13	129:1-8	17:1
12	I Kings 9:1-10:29	Acts 8:14-40	130:1-8	17:2-3
13	I Kings 11:1-12:19	Acts 9:1-25	131:1-3	17:4-5
14	I Kings 12:20-13:34	Acts 9:26:43	132:1-18	17:6
15	I Kings 14:1-15:24	Acts 10:1-23	133:1-3	17:7-8
16	I Kings 15:25-17:24	Acts 10:24-48	134:1-3	17:9-11
17	I Kings 18:1-46	Acts 11:1-30	135:1-21	17:12-13
18	I Kings 19:1-21	Acts 12:1-24	136:1-26	17:14-15
19	I Kings 20:1-21:29	Acts 12:25-13:12	137:1-9	17:16
20	I Kings 22:1-53	Acts 13:13-41	138:1-8	17:17-18
21	II Kings 1:1-2:25	Acts 13:42-14:7	139:1-24	17:19-21
22	II Kings 3:1-4:17	Acts 14:8-28	140:1-13	17:22
23	II Kings 4:18-5:27	Acts 15:1-29	141:1-10	17:23
24	II Kings 6:1-7:20	Acts 15:30-16:15	142:1-7	17:24-25
25	II Kings 8:1-9:13	Acts 16:16-40	143:1-12	17:26
26	II Kings 9:14-10:31	Acts 17:1-34	144:1-15	17:27-28
27	II Kings 10:32-12:21	Acts 18:1-23	145:1-21	18:1
28	II Kings 13:1-14:29	Acts 18:24-19:10	146:1-10	18:2-3
29	II Kings 15:1-16:20	Acts 19:11-41	147:1-20	18:4-5
30	II Kings 17:1-18:16	Acts 20:1-38	148:1-14	18:6-7

KEY PASSAGES

_____
_____
_____
_____
_____
_____
_____
_____
_____
_____
_____
_____
_____

PRAYER REQUESTS

Date: **Request:**   **Date Answered:**
_____
_____
_____
_____
_____
_____
_____
_____
_____
_____
_____
_____
_____
_____
_____
_____
_____
_____

JUNE 2019

Sunday	Monday	Tuesday	Wednesday
2	3	4	5
9	10	11	12
16 Father's Day	17	18	19
23 30	24	25	26

Thursday	Friday	Saturday
		1
6	7	8
13	14	15
20	21	22
27	28	29

Notes
_____
_____
_____
_____
_____
_____
_____
_____
_____
_____
_____
_____
_____
_____
_____
_____
_____
_____
_____
_____
_____
_____
_____
_____
_____
_____
_____
_____
_____
_____
_____
_____
_____

JULY 2019

	Old Testament	New Testament	Psalms	Proverbs
1	II Kings 18:17-19:37	Acts 21:1-14	149:1-9	18:8
2	II Kings 20:1-22:2	Acts 21:15-36	150:1-6	18:9-10
3	II Kings 22:3-23:30	Acts 21:37-22:16	1:1-6	18:11-12
4	II Kings 23:31-25:30	Acts 22:17-23:10	2:1-12	18:13
5	I Chron 1:1-2:17	Acts 23:11-35	3:1-8	18:14-15
6	I Chron 2:18-4:8	Acts 24:1-27	4:1-8	18:16-18
7	I Chron 4:9-5:10	Acts 25:1-27	5:1-12	18:19
8	I Chron 5:11-6:81	Acts 26:1-32	6:1-10	18:20-21
9	I Chron 7:1-8:40	Acts 27:1-20	7:1-17	18:22
10	I Chron 9:1-10:14	Acts 27:21-44	8:1-9	18:23-24
11	I Chron 11:1-12:22	Acts 28:1-31	9:1-10	19:1-3
12	I Chron 12:23-14:17	Rom 1:1-17	9:11-20	19:4-5
13	I Chron 15:1-16:36	Rom 1:18-32	10:1-7	19:6-7
14	I Chron 16:37-18:17	Rom 2:1-24	10:8-18	19:8-9
15	I Chron 19:1-21:30	Rom 2:25-3:8	11:1-7	19:10-12
16	I Chron 22:1-23:32	Rom 3:9-31	12:1-8	19:13-14
17	I Chron 24:1-26:11	Rom 4:1-12	13:1-6	19:15-16
18	I Chron 26:12-27:34	Rom 4:13-5:2	14:1-7	19:17
19	I Chron 28:1-29:30	Rom 5:3-21	15:1-5	19:18-19
20	II Chron 1:1-3:17	Rom 6:1-23	16:1-11	19:20-21
21	II Chron 4:1-6:11	Rom 7:1-13	17:1-15	19:22-23
22	II Chron 6:12-8:10	Rom 7:13-8:11	18:1-15	19:24-25
23	II Chron 8:11-10:19	Rom 8:12-25	18:16-34	19:26
24	II Chron 11:1-13:22	Rom 8:26-39	18:35-50	19:27-29
25	II Chron 14:1-16:14	Rom 9:1-24	19:1-14	20:1
26	II Chron 17:1-18:34	Rom 9:25-10:13	20:1-9	20:2-3
27	II Chron 19:1-20:37	Rom 10:14-11:10	21:1-13	20:4-6
28	II Chron 21:1-23:21	Rom 11:11-36	22:1-15	20:07
29	II Chron 24:1-25:28	Rom 12:1-21	22:16-31	20:8-10
30	II Chron 26:1-28:27	Rom 13:1-14	23:1-6	20:11
31	II Chron 29:1-36	Rom 14:1-23	24:1-10	20:12

KEY PASSAGES

_____
_____
_____
_____
_____
_____
_____
_____
_____
_____
_____
_____

PRAYER REQUESTS

Date: **Request:**   **Date Answered:**

_____
_____
_____
_____
_____
_____
_____
_____
_____
_____
_____
_____
_____
_____
_____
_____
_____

JULY 2019

Sunday	Monday	Tuesday	Wednesday
	1	2	3
7	8	9	10
14	15	16	17
21	22	23	24
28	29	30	31

Thursday	Friday	Saturday	Notes
4	5	6	
Independence Day			
11	12	13	
18	19	20	
25	26	27	

AUGUST 2019

	Old Testament	New Testament	Psalms	Proverbs
1	II Chron 30:1-31:21	Rom 15:1-21	25:1-11	20:13-15
2	II Chron 32:1-33:9	Rom 15:22-16:7	25:12-22	20:16-18
3	II Chron 33:10-34:33	Rom 16:8-27	26:1-12	20:19
4	II Chron 35:1-36:23	I Cor 1:1-17	27:1-6	20:20-21
5	Ezra 1:1-2:70	I Cor 1:18-2:5	27:7-14	20:22-23
6	Ezra 3:1-4:24	I Cor 2:6-3:4	28:1-9	20:24-25
7	Ezra 5:1-6:22	I Cor 3:5-23	29:1-11	20:26-27
8	Ezra 7:1-8:20	I Cor 4:1-21	30:1-12	20:28-30
9	Ezra 8:21-9:15	I Cor 5:1-13	31:1-8	21:1-2
10	Ezra 10:1-44	I Cor 6:1-20	31:9-18	21:3
11	Neh 1:1-3:14	I Cor 7:1-24	31:19-24	21:4
12	Neh 3:15-5:13	I Cor 7:25-40	32:1-11	21:5-7
13	Neh 5:14-7:60	I Cor 8:1-13	33:1-12	21:8-10
14	Neh 7:61-9:21	I Cor 9:1-18	33:13-22	21:11-12
15	Neh 9:22-10:39	I Cor 9:19-10:13	34:1-10	21:13
16	Neh 11:1-12:26	I Cor 10:14-11:1	34:11-22	21:14-16
17	Neh 12:27-13:31	I Cor 11:2-16	35:1-16	21:17-18
18	Esther 1:1-3:15	I Cor 11:17-34	35:17-28	21:19-20
19	Esther 4:1-7:10	I Cor 12:1-26	36:1-12	21:21-22
20	Esther 8:1-10:3	I Cor 12:27-13:13	37:1-11	21:23-24
21	Job 1:1-3:26	I Cor 14:1-17	37:12-24	21:25-26
22	Job 4:1-7:21	I Cor 14:18-40	37:25-40	21:27
23	Job 8:1-11:20	I Cor 15:1-28	38:1-22	21:28-29
24	Job 12:1-15:35	I Cor 15:29-58	39:1-13	21:30-31
25	Job 16:1-19:29	I Cor 16:1-24	40:1-10	22:1
26	Job 20:1-22:30	II Cor 1:1-11	40:11-17	22:2-4
27	Job 23:1-27:23	II Cor 1:12-22	41:1-13	22:5-6
28	Job 28:1-30:31	II Cor 1:23-2:17	42:1-11	22:7
29	Job 31:1-33:33	II Cor 3:1-18	43:1-5	22:8-9
30	Job 34:1-36:33	II Cor 4:1-15	44:1-8	22:10-12
31	Job 37:1-39:30	II Cor 4:16-5:11	44:9-26	22:13

KEY PASSAGES

PRAYER REQUESTS

Date: **Request:**   **Date Answered:**

AUGUST 2019

Sunday	Monday	Tuesday	Wednesday
4	5	6	7
11	12 New Song Nashville's Anniversary (1993 - 2019)	13	14
18	19	20	21
25	26	27	28

Thursday	Friday	Saturday
1	2	3
8	9	10
15	16	17
22	23	24
29	30	31

Notes

SEPTEMBER 2019

	Old Testament	New Testament	Psalms	Proverbs
1	Job 40:1-42:17	II Cor 5:12-21	45:1-17	22:14
2	Eccl 1:1-3:22	II Cor 6:1-10	46:1-11	22:15
3	Eccl 4:1-6:12	II Cor 6:11-7:7	47:1-9	22:16
4	Eccl 7:1-9:18	II Cor 7:8-16	48:1-14	22:17-19
5	Eccl 10:1-12:14	II Cor 8:1-15	49:1-20	22:20-21
6	Song 1:1-4:16	II Cor 8:16-24	50:1-23	22:22-23
7	Song 5:1-8:14	II Cor 9:1-15	51:1-19	22:24-25
8	Isaiah 1:1-2:22	II Cor 10:1-18	52:1-9	22:26-27
9	Isaiah 3:1-5:30	II Cor 11:1-15	53:1-6	22:28-29
10	Isaiah 6:1-7:25	II Cor 11:16-33	54:1-7	23:1-3
11	Isaiah 8:1-9:21	II Cor 12:1-10	55:1-23	23:4-5
12	Isaiah 10:1-11:16	II Cor 12:11-21	56:1-13	23:6-8
13	Isaiah 12:1-14:32	II Cor 13:1-14	57:1-11	23:9-11
14	Isaiah 15:1-18:7	Gal 1:1-24	58:1-11	23:12
15	Isaiah 19:1-21:17	Gal 2:1-16	59:1-17	23:13-14
16	Isaiah 22:1-24:23	Gal 2:17-3:9	60:1-12	23:15-16
17	Isaiah 25:1-28:15	Gal 3:10-25	61:1-8	23:17-18
18	Isaiah 28:16-30:11	Gal 3:26-4:31	62:1-12	23:19-21
19	Isaiah 30:12-33:9	Gal 5:1-15	63:1-11	23:22
20	Isaiah 33:10-36:22	Gal 5:16-26	64:1-10	23:23
21	Isaiah 37:1-38:22	Gal 6:1-18	65:1-13	23:24
22	Isaiah 39:1-41:20	Eph 1:1-23	66:1-20	23:25-28
23	Isaiah 41:21-43:21	Eph 2:1-22	67:1-7	23:29-35
24	Isaiah 43:22-45:13	Eph 3:1-21	68:1-18	24:1-2
25	Isaiah 45:14-48:11	Eph 4:1-16	68:19-35	24:3-4
26	Isaiah 48:12-50:11	Eph 4:17-32	69:1-18	24:5-6
27	Isaiah 51:1-53:12	Eph 5:1-33	69:19-36	24:7
28	Isaiah 54:1-57:13	Eph 6:1-24	70:1-5	24:8
29	Isaiah 57:14-59:21	Phil 1:1-26	71:1-24	24:9-10
30	Isaiah 60:1-62:5	Phil 1:27-2:18	72:1-20	24:11-12

KEY PASSAGES

_____
_____
_____
_____
_____
_____
_____
_____
_____
_____
_____
_____
_____
_____

PRAYER REQUESTS

Date: **Request:**   **Date Answered:**

_____
_____
_____
_____
_____
_____
_____
_____
_____
_____
_____
_____
_____
_____
_____
_____
_____
_____

SEPTEMBER 2019

Sunday	Monday	Tuesday	Wednesday
1	2 Labor Day	3	4
8	9	10	11 Patriot Day
15	16	17	18
22	23	24	25
29	30		

Thursday	Friday	Saturday
5	6	7
12	13	14
19	20	21
26	27	28

OCTOBER 2019

	Old Testament	New Testament	Psalms	Proverbs
1	Isaiah 62:6-64:12	Phil 2:19-3:6	73:1-28	24:13-14
2	Isaiah 65:1-66:24	Phil 3:7-4:1	74:1-23	24:15-16
3	Jer 1:1-2:30	Phil 4:2-23	75:1-10	24:17-20
4	Jer 2:31-4:18	Col 1:1-23	76:1-12	24:21-22
5	Jer 4:19-6:15	Col 1:24-2:10	77:1-20	24:23-25
6	Jer 6:16-8:7	Col 2:11-23	78:1-31	24:26
7	Jer 8:8-9:26	Col 3:1-17	78:32-55	24:27
8	Jer 10:1-11:23	Col 3:18-4:18	78:56-72	24:28-29
9	Jer 12:1-14:10	I Thes 1:1-2:12	79:1-13	24:30-34
10	Jer 14:11-16:13	I Thes 2:13-3:13	80:1-19	25:1-5
11	Jer 16:14-18:23	I Thes 4:1-5:3	81:1-16	25:6-7
12	Jer 19:1-21:14	I Thes 5:4-28	82:1-8	25:8-10
13	Jer 22:1-23:20	II Thes 1:1-12	83:1-18	25:11-13
14	Jer 23:21-25:38	II Thes 2:1-17	84:1-12	25:14-15
15	Jer 26:1-27:22	II Thes 3:1-18	85:1-13	25:16
16	Jer 28:1-29:32	I Tim 1:1-20	86:1-17	25:17
17	Jer 30:1-31:22	I Tim 2:1-15	87:1-7	25:18-19
18	Jer 31:23-32:44	I Tim 3:1-16	88:1-18	25:20-22
19	Jer 33:1-34:22	I Tim 4:1-16	89:1-18	25:23-24
20	Jer 35:1-36:32	I Tim 5:1-25	89:19-37	25:25-27
21	Jer 37:1-38:28	I Tim 6:1-21	89:38-52	25:28
22	Jer 39:1-41:18	II Tim 1:1-18	90:1-91:16	26:1-2
23	Jer 42:1-44:23	II Tim 2:1-21	92:1-93:5	26:3-5
24	Jer 44:24-47:7	II Tim 2:22-3:17	94:1-23	26:6-8
25	Jer 48:1-49:22	II Tim 4:1-22	95:1-96:13	26:9-12
26	Jer 49:23-50:46	Titus 1:1-16	97:1-98:9	26:13-16
27	Jer 51:1-53	Titus 2:1-15	99:1-9	26:17
28	Jer 51:54-52:34	Titus 3:1-15	100:1-5	26:18-19
29	Lam 1:1-2:22	Phile 1-25	101:1-8	26:20
30	Lam 3:1-66	Heb 1:1-14	102:1-28	26:21-22
31	Lam 4-5:22	Heb. 2:1-18	103:1-22	26:23

KEY PASSAGES

_____
_____
_____
_____
_____
_____
_____
_____
_____
_____
_____
_____
_____
_____
_____

PRAYER REQUESTS

Date: **Request:**   **Date Answered:**

_____
_____
_____
_____
_____
_____
_____
_____
_____
_____
_____
_____
_____
_____
_____
_____
_____
_____

OCTOBER 2019

Sunday	Monday	Tuesday	Wednesday
	1	2	3
7	8 Columbus Day	9	10
14	15	16	17
21	22	23	24
28	29	30	31

Thursday	Friday	Saturday
4	5	6
11	12	13
18	19	20
25	26	27

NOVEMBER 2019

	Old Testament	New Testament	Psalms	Proverbs
1	Eze 1:1-3:15	Heb 3:1-19	104:1-18	26:24-26
2	Eze 3:16-6:14	Heb 4:1-16	104:19-35	26:27
3	Eze 7:1-9:11	Heb 5:1-14	105:1-15	26:28
4	Eze 10:1-11:25	Heb 6:1-20	105:16-36	27:1-2
5	Eze 12:1-14:11	Heb 7:1-17	105:37-45	27:3
6	Eze 14:12-16:43	Heb 7:18-28	106:1-23	27:4-6
7	Eze 16:44-17:24	Heb 8:1-13	106:24-48	27:7-9
8	Eze 18:1-19:14	Heb 9:1-15	107:1-16	27:10
9	Eze 20:1-49	Heb 9:16-28	107:17-43	27:11
10	Eze 21:1-22:31	Heb 10:1-18	108:1-13	27:12
11	Eze 23:1-49	Heb 10:19-39	109:1-31	27:13
12	Eze 24:1-26:21	Heb 11:1-16	110:1-7	27:14
13	Eze 27:1-28:26	Heb 11:17-29	111:1-10	27:15-16
14	Eze 29:1-30:26	Heb 11:30-12:11	112:1-10	27:17
15	Eze 31:1-32:32	Heb 12:12-29	113:1-114:8	27:18-20
16	Eze 33:1-34:31	Heb 13:1-25	115:1-18	27:21-22
17	Eze 35:1-36:38	James 1:1-18	116:1-19	27:23-27
18	Eze 37:1-38:23	James 1:19-2:13	117:1-2	28:1
19	Eze 39:1-40:27	James 2:14-3:18	118:1-18	28:2
20	Eze 40:28-41:26	James 4:1-17	118:19-29	28:3-5
21	Eze 42:1-43:27	James 5:1-20	119:1-16	28:6-7
22	Eze 44:1-45:9	I Pet 1:1-12	119:17-32	28:8-10
23	Eze 45:10-46:24	I Pet 1:13-2:10	119:33-48	28:11
24	Eze 47:1-48:35	I Pet 2:11-3:7	119:49-64	28:12-13
25	Dan 1:1-2:23	I Pet 3:8-4:6	119:65-80	28:14
26	Dan 2:24-3:30	I Pet 4:7-5:14	119:81-96	28:15-16
27	Dan 4:1-37	II Pet 1:1-21	119:97-112	28:17-18
28	Dan 5:1-31	II Pet 2:1-22	119:113-128	28:19-20
29	Dan 6:1-28	II Pet 3:1-18	119:129-152	28:21-22
30	Dan 7:1-28	I John 1:1-10	119:153-176	28:23-24

KEY PASSAGES

_____
_____
_____
_____
_____
_____
_____
_____
_____
_____
_____
_____

PRAYER REQUESTS

Date: **Request:**   **Date Answered:**

_____
_____
_____
_____
_____
_____
_____
_____
_____
_____
_____
_____
_____
_____
_____
_____
_____
_____
_____

NOVEMBER 2019

Sunday	Monday	Tuesday	Wednesday
3 Daylight Saving (End)	4	5	6
10	11 Veterans Day	12	13
17	18	19	20
24	25	26	27

Thursday	Friday	Saturday
	1	2
7	8	9
14	15	16
21	22	23
Thanksgiving		
28	29	30

Notes

_____
_____
_____
_____
_____
_____
_____
_____
_____
_____
_____
_____
_____
_____
_____
_____
_____
_____
_____
_____
_____
_____
_____
_____
_____
_____
_____
_____
_____

DECEMBER 2019

	Old Testament	New Testament	Psalms	Proverbs
1	Dan 8:1-27	I John 2:1-17	120:1-7	28:25-26
2	Dan 9:1-11:1	I John 2:18-3:9	121:1-8	28:27-28
3	Dan 11:2-45	I John 3:10-24	122:1-9	29:1
4	Dan 12:1-13	I John 4:1-21	123:1-4	29:2-4
5	Hosea 1:1-3:5	I John 5:1-21	124:1-8	29:5-8
6	Hosea 4:1-5:15	II John 1-13	125:1-5	29:9-11
7	Hosea 6:1-9:17	III John 1-14	126:1-6	29:12-14
8	Hosea 10:1-14:9	Jude 1-25	127:1-5	29:15-17
9	Joel 1:1-3:21	Rev 1:1-20	128:1-6	29:18
10	Amos 1:1-3:15	Rev 2:1-17	129:1-8	29:19-20
11	Amos 4:1-6:14	Rev 2:18-3:6	130:1-8	29:21-22
12	Amos 7:1-9:15	Rev 3:7-22	131:1-3	29:23
13	Obadiah 1-21	Rev 4:1-11	132:1-18	29:24-25
14	Jonah 1:1-4:11	Rev. 5:1-14	133:1-3	29:26-27
15	Micah 1:1-4:13	Rev 6:1-17	134:1-3	30:1-4
16	Micah 5:1-7:20	Rev 7:1-17	135:1-21	30:5-6
17	Nahum 1:1-3:19	Rev 8:1-13	136:1-26	30:7-9
18	Habakkuk 1:1-3:19	Rev 9:1-21	137:1-9	30:10
19	Zeph. 1:1-3:20	Rev 10:1-11	138:1-8	30:11-14
20	Haggai 1:1-2:23	Rev 11:1-19	139:1-24	30:15-16
21	Zech 1:1-21	Rev 12:1-17	140:1-13	30:17
22	Zech 2:1-3:10	Rev 13:1-18	141:1-10	30:18-20
23	Zech 4:1-5:11	Rev 14:1-20	142:1-7	30:21-23
24	Zech 6:1-7:14	Rev 15:1-8	143:1-12	30:24-28
25	Zech 8:1-23	Rev 16:1-21	144:1-15	30:29-31
26	Zech 9:1-17	Rev 17:1-18	145:1-21	30:32
27	Zech 10:1-11:17	Rev 18:1-24	146:1-10	30:33
28	Zech 12:1-13:9	Rev 19:1-21	147:1-20	31:1-7
29	Zech 14:1-21	Rev 20:1-15	148:1-14	31:8-9
30	Malachi 1:1-2:17	Rev 21:1-27	149:1-9	31:10-24
31	Malachi 3:1-4:6	Rev 22:1-21	150:1-6	31:25-31

KEY PASSAGES

_____
_____
_____
_____
_____
_____
_____
_____
_____
_____
_____
_____
_____

PRAYER REQUESTS

Date: **Request:**   **Date Answered:**

_____
_____
_____
_____
_____
_____
_____
_____
_____
_____
_____
_____
_____
_____
_____
_____
_____
_____
_____
_____

DECEMBER 2019

Sunday	Monday	Tuesday	Wednesday
1	2	3	4
8	9	10	11
15	16	17	18
22	23	24	25 Christmas Day
29	30	31 New Year's Eve	

	Thursday	Friday	Saturday
	5	6	7
	12	13	14
	19	20	21
	26	27	28

Notes

_____
_____
_____
_____
_____
_____
_____
_____
_____
_____
_____
_____
_____
_____
_____
_____
_____
_____
_____
_____
_____
_____
_____
_____
_____
_____
_____
_____
_____
_____
_____
_____

January
6th 2019

at church
w/ my four Nashville Boys

purpouseful - everybody
- greeters
- mix race couple
- person of color in,
New Song

I want to give Gavin
a turn too, tournament
is too noisy

— the Word of God

or the God of the

Word
~~~~~~~~~~~~~
— Churches at the Branch?

Polly?   Liz?

Pat?
~~~~~~~~~~~~~

light
saber

BY: GAVEN

Date:

Bell   February 10, 2019

Cross Point - Bep's church
                - Pastor Kevin
          - Pete + Eden
    - get out prayer list
    - fast
      - suzy
    - Donna

Matt 3:1-   no prophetic utterance
             for 400 years - silence

My Deliveror is coming
              is standing nigh

            noya
meta   mise
change of mind ⎫ REPENT
"about face!" ⎭

    - two things of same value

    REPENT

CHANGE!

Begin	End
repent	repent
about face	change

Acts 2: ~~XX~~ 27 - REPENT

    17 - God says REPENT

NOT OF GOD → TO WHAT
                 OR WHO is
                 GOD

Judas (Bill) - change

"I'm sorry!"

turn (to) Grief, sorrow

       - is not repentance

     ⊘ - all that (is) God

CHANGE → thinking

          see, repent, turn
             to God

matt. 27:3

- feeling bad
- crying
- saying "I'm sorrow"
- altar call shameful
- rededication
  to "the Lord"

} not repentance

〰〰〰〰〰〰〰〰〰〰〰

allow my thinking to

line up with God and the

WORD of God

- ~~adi~~ ~~DAAbb~~ Daily
- meditate on HIS PROMISES

think rightly Believe fully

Taking every thought captive
to the obedience of Christ

BODY - visible + Physical
part that will be
reser
Spirit urrected joined to spirit
and soul eternal
Soul

(Body)   Romans 2l ll
                                   12:1

1 Cor 6:12

keeping a pure Body
drugs, alcohol, abusive
food

"He's not done with you, Becky"

         Ashley Hagen

① stewardship - for Him
     with him

② strengthening - Body
     will come into alignment
③ strategy - seek God

"How am I supposed
   to get there and
   stay there"

Praying + Praising

Treasures / not tricks

Matt 14:19, 26:26

(New Wine)

Luke 11   Our Father

Pray - thanking
       - Hallowed be Thy name

Is any among you sick?

I'm sick and believing for
healing

IN DUE SEASON

Pray, Discern, Praise, vocal

exploits - future

rejoice

who reigns over me

physical and in the
spirit

Sacificing + suffering

Celibrate - love to eat

① suffering 3rd World problems

① problems - all will suffer

        - pain is bad

meth
alcohol
weed

" Just forget (the pain) "

too much affiction

② FULL of JOY | PEACE

sacrificing - willingly giving up

- something, someone

for the glory of God

good of others

Phil 2:5   ②

I was one half but now
i am one hole

Befor

Danika

after

Sierra draws a heart in church

8/98·18/19

Hello Danika,

It is a blessing to see you today as you are growing more beautiful each year. May you love Jesus more & more in the days & years ahead, His plan for you is so wonderful! Trust & obey Him and have a successful life.

I love U,

Date:

Humble - empty, abase
Him
and
became obedient

to the point of death

call - Maryanne
Yonkees - molly
Suzanne
Doctors
Volunteer

this
week

4

therefore
ALL

ALL

God has exalted Him
ABOVE EVERYTHING

5

Date:

Date:

Date:

Date:

Date:

Date:

Date:

Date:

Date: _____

Date:

Date:

Date:

Date:

Date:

Date:

Date:

Date:

Date:

Date:

Date:

Date:

Date:

Date:

Date:

Date:

Date:

Date:

Date:

Date:

Date:

Date:

Date:

Date:

Date:

Date:

Date:

Date:

Date:

Date:

Date:

Date:

Date:

Date:

Date:

Date:

Date:

Date:

Date:

Date:

Date:

Date:

Date:

Date:

Date:

Date:

Date:

Date:

Date:

Date:

Date:

Date:

Date:

Date:

Date:

Date:

Date:

Date:

Date:

Date:

Date:

Date:

Date:

Date:

Date:

Date:

Date:

Date:

Date:

Date:

Date:

Date:

Date:

Date:

Date:

Date:

Date:

Date:

Date:

Date: _____

Date:

Date: _____

Mulberry Clinic

Dr. Timothy Caraher MD

Theron Hutton

615-794-0500

Karen Knapp

615- 979-1788

967 - 0371

2020

January

Sun	Mon	Tue	Wed	Thu	Fri	Sat
29	30	31	1	2	3	4
5	6	7	8	9	10	11
12	13	14	15	16	17	18
19	20	21	22	23	24	25
26	27	28	29	30	31	1
2	3	4	5	6	7	8

February

Sun	Mon	Tue	Wed	Thu	Fri	Sat
26	27	28	29	30	31	1
2	3	4	5	6	7	8
9	10	11	12	13	14	15
16	17	18	19	20	21	22
23	24	25	26	27	28	29
1	2	3	4	5	6	7

March

Sun	Mon	Tue	Wed	Thu	Fri	Sat
1	2	3	4	5	6	7
8	9	10	11	12	13	14
15	16	17	18	19	20	21
22	23	24	25	26	27	28
29	30	31	1	2	3	4
5	6	7	8	9	10	11

April

Sun	Mon	Tue	Wed	Thu	Fri	Sat
29	30	31	1	2	3	4
5	6	7	8	9	10	11
12	13	14	15	16	17	18
19	20	21	22	23	24	25
26	27	28	29	30	1	2
3	4	5	6	7	8	9

May

Sun	Mon	Tue	Wed	Thu	Fri	Sat
26	27	28	29	30	1	2
3	4	5	6	7	8	9
10	11	12	13	14	15	16
17	18	19	20	21	22	23
24	25	26	27	28	29	30
31	1	2	3	4	5	6

June

Sun	Mon	Tue	Wed	Thu	Fri	Sat
31	1	2	3	4	5	6
7	8	9	10	11	12	13
14	15	16	17	18	19	20
21	22	23	24	25	26	27
28	29	30	1	2	3	4
5	6	7	8	9	10	11

July

Sun	Mon	Tue	Wed	Thu	Fri	Sat
28	29	30	1	2	3	4
5	6	7	8	9	10	11
12	13	14	15	16	17	18
19	20	21	22	23	24	25
26	27	28	29	30	31	1
2	3	4	5	6	7	8

August

Sun	Mon	Tue	Wed	Thu	Fri	Sat
26	27	28	29	30	31	1
2	3	4	5	6	7	8
9	10	11	12	13	14	15
16	17	18	19	20	21	22
23	24	25	26	27	28	29
30	31	1	2	3	4	5

September

Sun	Mon	Tue	Wed	Thu	Fri	Sat
30	31	1	2	3	4	5
6	7	8	9	10	11	12
13	14	15	16	17	18	19
20	21	22	23	24	25	26
27	28	29	30	1	2	3
4	5	6	7	8	9	10

October

Sun	Mon	Tue	Wed	Thu	Fri	Sat
27	28	29	30	1	2	3
4	5	6	7	8	9	10
11	12	13	14	15	16	17
18	19	20	21	22	23	24
25	26	27	28	29	30	31
1	2	3	4	5	6	7

November

Sun	Mon	Tue	Wed	Thu	Fri	Sat
1	2	3	4	5	6	7
8	9	10	11	12	13	14
15	16	17	18	19	20	21
22	23	24	25	26	27	28
29	30	1	2	3	4	5
6	7	8	9	10	11	12

December

Sun	Mon	Tue	Wed	Thu	Fri	Sat
29	30	1	2	3	4	5
6	7	8	9	10	11	12
13	14	15	16	17	18	19
20	21	22	23	24	25	26
27	28	29	30	31	1	2
3	4	5	6	7	8	9

Made in the USA
Columbia, SC
30 November 2018